D1708490

To ....
From ....

NOTE

NOTE

NOTE

Bookmarks Coloring: Flowers and Pattern design: Pretty bookmarks to color: relax your mind and soul for beautiful bookmarks

Copyright: Published in the United States by Jenny Finn
Published September 2017

ISBN-13: 978-1977760883

ISBN-10: 1977760880

Merry Christmas

Merry Christmas

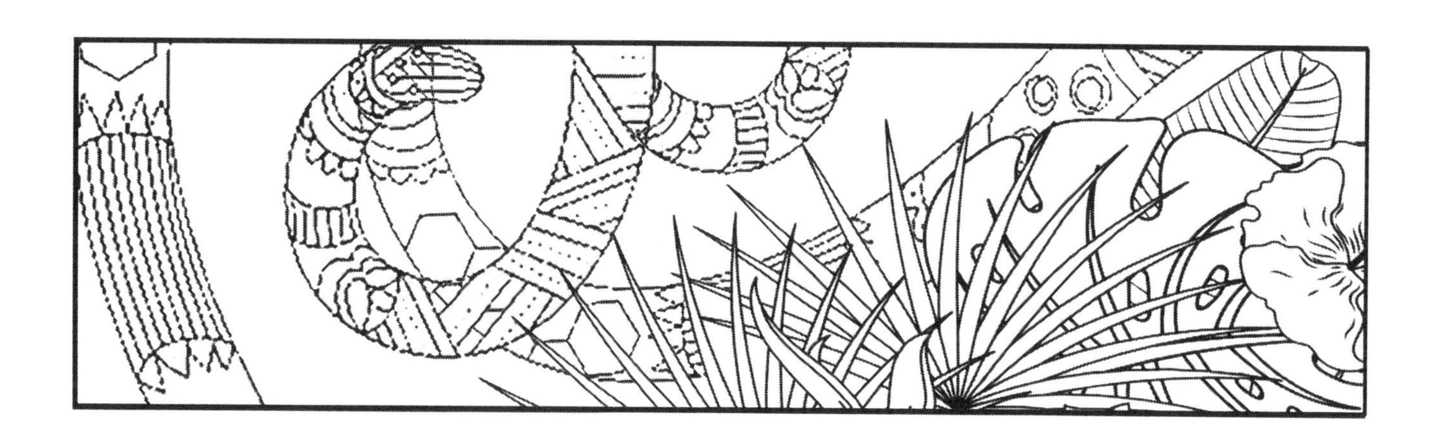

Made in the USA
San Bernardino, CA
27 March 2018